The Big Book Of
Torch Songs

The Big Book Of
Torch Songs

HLE

Hal Leonard Europe
Distributed by Music Sales

Exclusive Distributors:
Music Sales Limited
8/9 Frith Street, London W1D 3JB, UK.

Order No. HLE90002528
ISBN 1-84609-134-9
This book © Copyright 2005 by Hal Leonard Europe

Cover design by Chloë Alexander
Cover photograph courtesy Rex Features/Redferns/Music Pictures.com
Printed in the USA

Your Guarantee of Quality
As publishers, we strive to produce every book to the highest
commercial standards.
The book has been carefully designed to minimise awkward
page turns and to make playing from it a real pleasure.
Throughout, the printing and binding have been planned to ensure a
sturdy, attractive publication which should give years of enjoyment.
If your copy fails to meet our high standards, please inform us
and we will gladly replace it.

www.musicsales.com

ALL ALONE AM I

English Lyric by ARTHUR ALTMAN
Original Lyric by JEAN IOANNIDIS
Music by M. HADJIDAKIS

ALL OR NOTHING AT ALL

Words by JACK LAWRENCE
Music by ARTHUR ALTMAN

ALL THE WAY

from THE JOKER IS WILD

Words by SAMMY CAHN
Music by JAMES VAN HEUSEN

ANGEL EYES

Words by EARL BRENT
Music by MATT DENNIS

Try to think _ that love's not a - round, _ still it's un - com - fort -'bly near.

My old heart _ ain't gain - in' no ground _ be - cause my An - gel Eyes ain't here. _

An - gel Eyes _ that old dev - il sent, _

BABY, WON'T YOU PLEASE COME HOME

Words and Music by CHARLES WARFIELD
and CLARENCE WILLIAMS

AS LONG AS HE NEEDS ME

from the Broadway Musical OLIVER!

Words and Music by
LIONEL BART

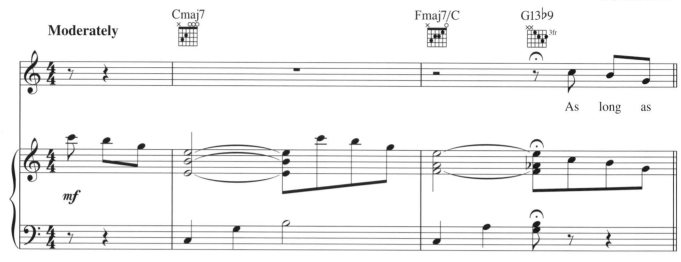

he needs me _____ I know where I must be, _____ I'll cling on
life is long, _____ I'll love him, right or wrong; _____ and some-how

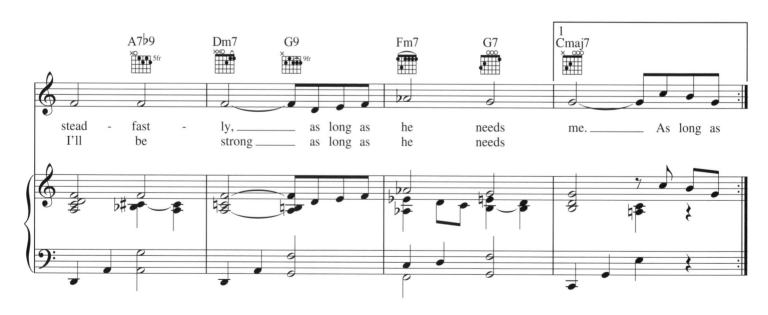

stead - fast - ly, _____ as long as he needs me. _____ As long as
I'll be strong _____ as long as he needs

BLACK COFFEE

Words and Music by PAUL FRANCIS WEBSTER
and SONNY BURKE

CAN'T HELP LOVIN' DAT MAN

from SHOW BOAT

Lyrics by OSCAR HAMMERSTEIN II
Music by JEROME KERN

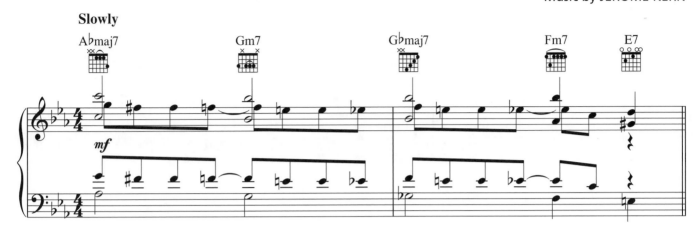

Fish got to swim___ and birds got to fly,___ I got to love___ one
Tell me he's la - zy, tell me he's slow,___ tell me I'm cra - zy,

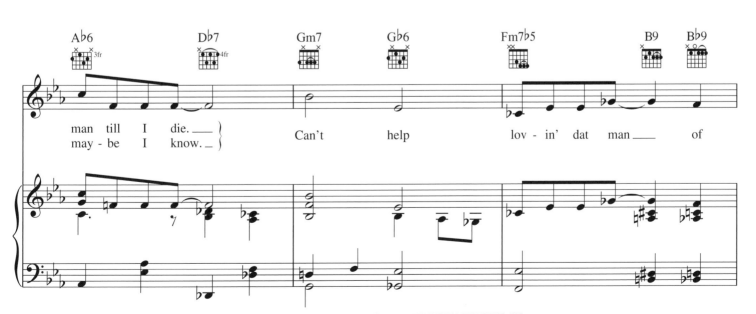

man till I die. ___ } Can't help lov - in' dat man___ of
may - be I know. ___ }

CRAZY

Words and Music by
WILLIE NELSON
Transcribed from Patsy Cline's recording

DO NOTHIN' TILL YOU HEAR FROM ME

Words and Music by DUKE ELLINGTON
and BOB RUSSELL

Moderately slow

Do noth-in' till you hear from me. Pay no at-ten-tion to what's said, why peo-ple tear the seam of an-y-one's dream is o-ver my head. Do noth-in' till you hear from

DON'T CRY OUT LOUD
(We Don't Cry Out Loud)

Words and Music by PETER ALLEN
and CAROLE BAYER SAGER

DON'T BLAME ME

Words by DOROTHY FIELDS
Music by JIMMY McHUGH

Ev-er since the luck-y night I found you ____ I've hung a-round you, ____ just like a
I like ev-'ry sin-gle thing a-bout you ____ with-out a doubt you ____ are like a

fool   fall-ing head and heels in   love like   a   kid   out   of
dream.   In my mind I find a   pic-ture   of   us   as   a

DON'T EXPLAIN

Words and Music by BILLIE HOLIDAY
and ARTHUR HERZOG

EAST OF THE SUN
(And West Of The Moon)

Words and Music by
BROOKS BOWMAN

THE END OF A LOVE AFFAIR

Words and Music by
EDWARD C. REDDING

smile on my face is-n't real - ly a smile at all? _____

___ So I smoke a lit - tle too much and I

drink a lit - tle too much, and the tunes I re-quest are not

al - ways the best, but the ones where the trum - pets blare! So I

FALLING IN LOVE AGAIN
(Can't Help It)
from the Paramount Picture THE BLUE ANGEL

Words by SAMMY LERNER
Music by FREDERICK HOLLANDER

EVERYTHING HAPPENS TO ME

Words by TOM ADAIR
Music by MATT DENNIS

FEVER

Words and Music by JOHN DAVENPORT
and EDDIE COOLEY

Moderately, with a beat

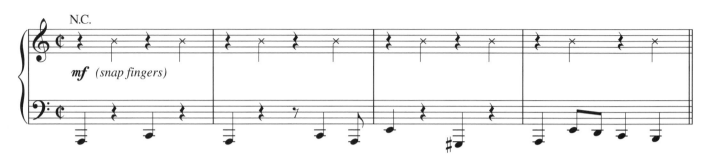

1. Nev - er know how much I love you, nev - er know how much I
2. Sun __ lights up the day - time, moon __ lights __ up __ the
3. Ro - me - o loved Ju - li - et. ___ Ju - li - et, she felt __ the
4. Cap - tain Smith and Po - ca - hon - tas had a ver - y mad __ af -
5. Now you've lis - tened to my sto - ry. Here's the point that I ___ have

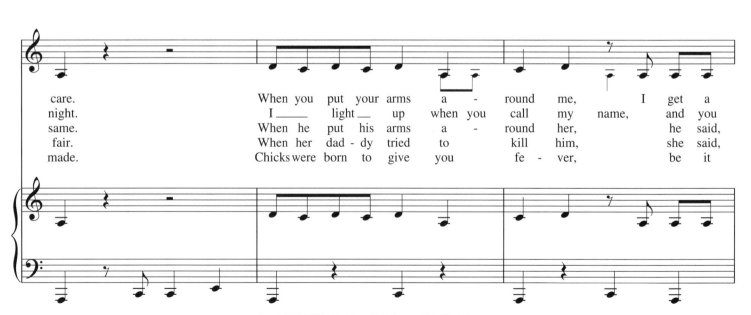

care. When you put your arms a - round me, I get a
night. I __ light __ up when you call my name, and you
same. When he put his arms a - round her, he said,
fair. When her dad - dy tried to kill him, she said,
made. Chicks were born to give you fe - ver, be it

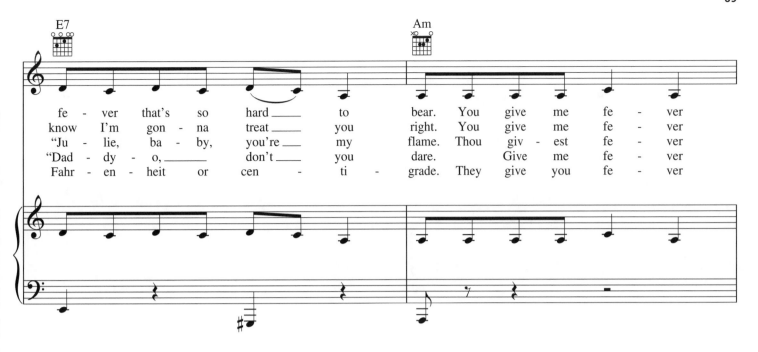

fe - ver that's so hard ___ to bear. You give me fe - ver
know I'm gon - na treat ___ you right. You give me fe - ver
"Ju - lie, ba - by, you're ___ my flame. Thou giv - est fe - ver
"Dad - dy - o, ___ don't ___ you dare. Give me fe - ver
Fahr - en - heit or cen - ti - grade. They give you fe - ver

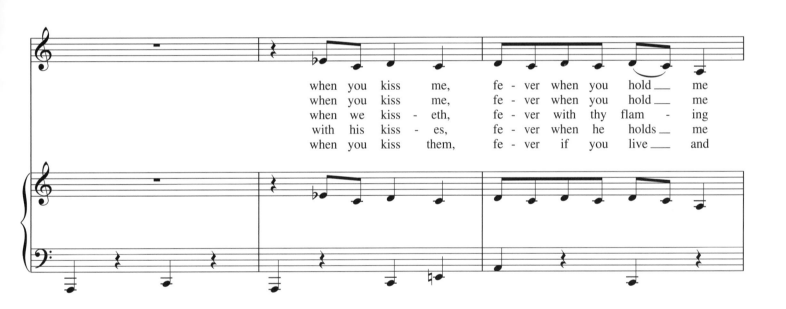

when you kiss me, fe - ver when you hold ___ me
when you kiss me, fe - ver when you hold ___ me
when we kiss - eth, fe - ver with thy flam - ing
with his kiss - es, fe - ver when he holds ___ me
when you kiss them, fe - ver if you live ___ and

tight, fe - ver in the morn - ing,
tight, fe - ver in the morn - ing,
youth. Fe - ver, I'm a - fire. ___
tight. Fe - ver, I'm his mis - sus. Oh,
learn. Fe - ver till you siz - zle,

70

FINE AND MELLOW

Words and Music by
BILLIE HOLIDAY

C7 C9 D♭9 C9 F Gm7 C7
low - est man that I've ev - er seen.
F D♭9 C7 C7♯5 Fm6 B♭7 B♭9
He wears high draped pants, stripes are real - ly yel -
F Gm7 F/A Gm7 F D♭dim F7/C F9 B♭
low. He wears high draped pants,
B♭9 F C7 F F♯dim
stripes are real - ly yel - low. But when he

FLY ME TO THE MOON
(In Other Words)
featured in the Motion Picture ONCE AROUND

Words and Music by
BART HOWARD

FOR ALL WE KNOW

Words by SAM M. LEWIS
Music by J. FRED COOTS

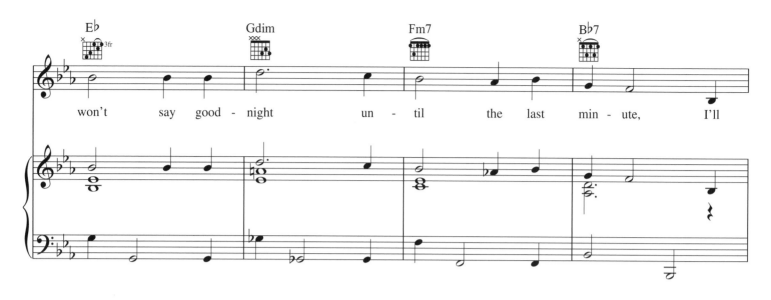

won't say good - night un - til the last min - ute, I'll

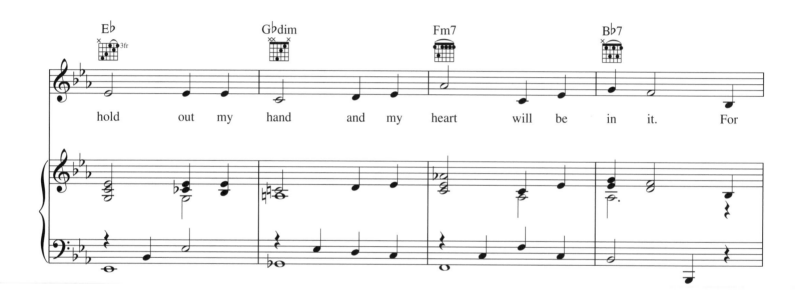

hold out my hand and my heart will be in it. For

all we know this may on - ly be a dream; We

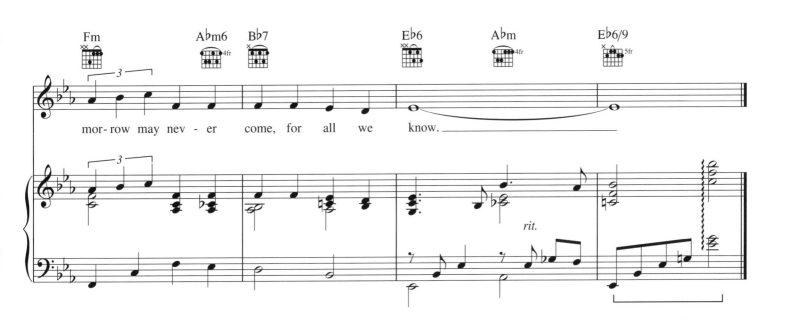

GOD BLESS' THE CHILD

from BUBBLING BROWN SUGAR

Words and Music by ARTHUR HERZOG JR.
and BILLIE HOLIDAY

Slowly, with feeling

Them that's got shall get, Them that's not shall lose, So the

Bi-ble said, And it still is news; Ma-ma may have, Pa-pa may have, But

God bless the child that's got his own! That's got his own. Yes, the

GOOD MORNING HEARTACHE

Words and Music by DAN FISHER,
IRENE HIGGINBOTHAM and ERVIN DRAKE

GOODBYE

Words and Music by
GORDON JENKINS

HERE'S THAT RAINY DAY
from CARNIVAL IN FLANDERS

Words by JOHNNY BURKE
Music by JIMMY VAN HEUSEN

GOODBYE TO LOVE

Words and Music by RICHARD CARPENTER
and JOHN BETTIS

A HOUSE IS NOT A HOME

Lyric by HAL DAVID
Music by BURT BACHARACH

Slowly and expressively

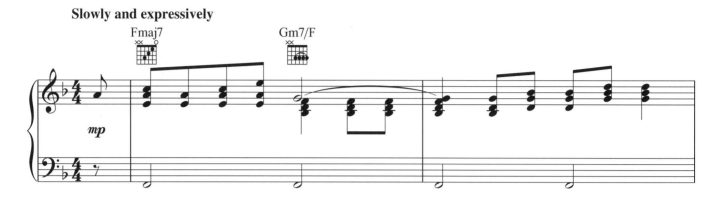

A chair is still a chair ____

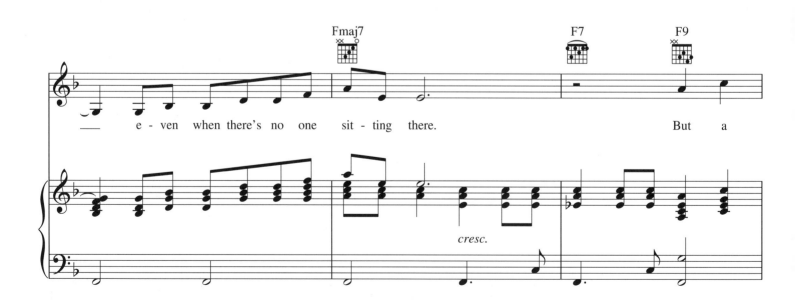

____ e-ven when there's no one sit-ting there. But a

HOW CAN YOU MEND A BROKEN HEART

Words and Music by ROBIN GIBB
and BARRY GIBB

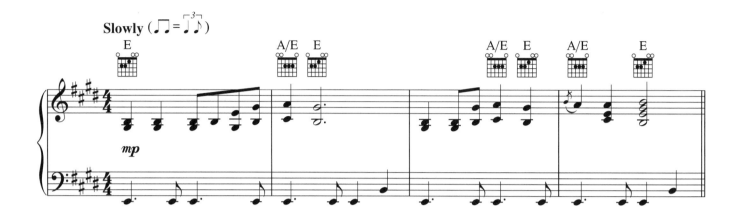

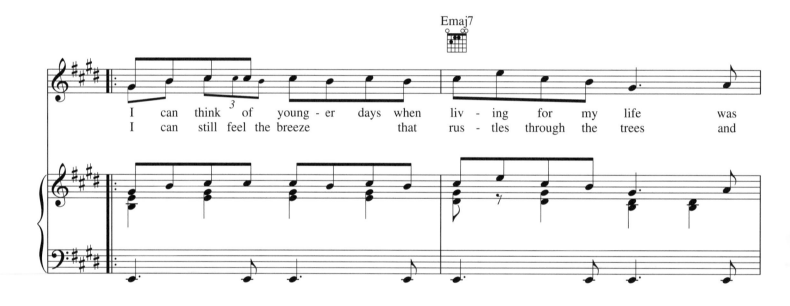

I can think of young-er days when liv-ing for my life was
I can still feel the breeze that rus-tles through the trees and

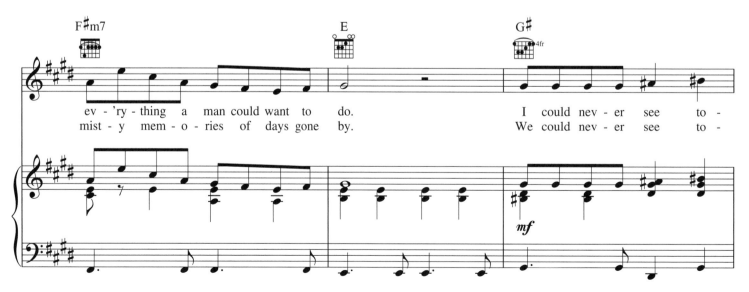

ev-'ry-thing a man could want to do. I could nev-er see to-
mist-y mem-o-ries of days gone by. We could nev-er see to-

I GET ALONG WITHOUT YOU VERY WELL
(Except Sometimes)

Words and Music by HOAGY CARMICHAEL
Inspired by a poem written by J.B. THOMPSON

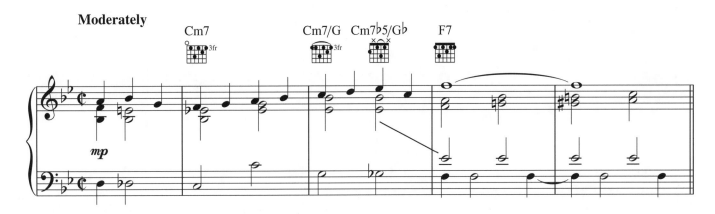

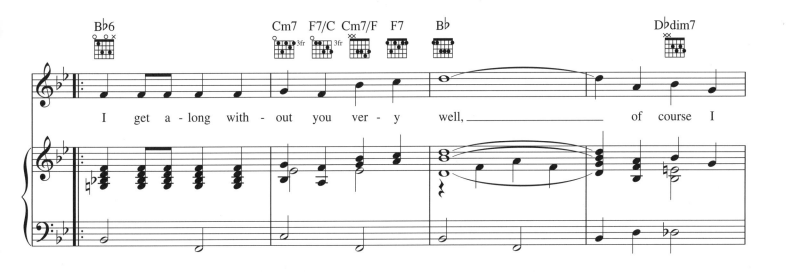

I get a-long with-out you ver-y well, _____ of course I

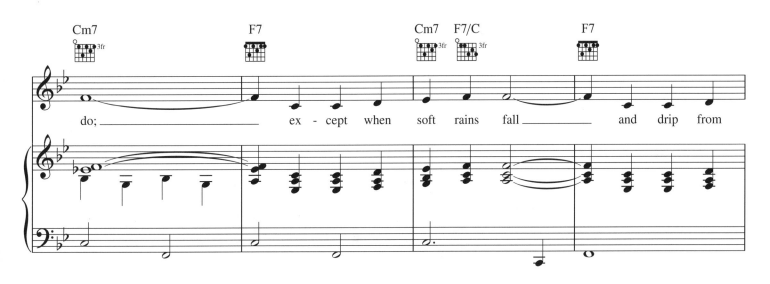

do; _____ ex-cept when soft rains fall _____ and drip from

HOW INSENSITIVE
(Insensatez)

Music by ANTONIO CARLOS JOBIM
Original Words by VINICIUS DE MORAES
English Words by NORMAN GIMBEL

How, _____ in-sen-si-tive _____
Now, _____ {he's she's} gone_ a-way, _____

_____ I must_ have seemed _____ when {he she} told me that_ {he she} loved_ me. _____
_____ and I'm a-lone _____ with the mem'ry of_ {his her} last_ look. _____

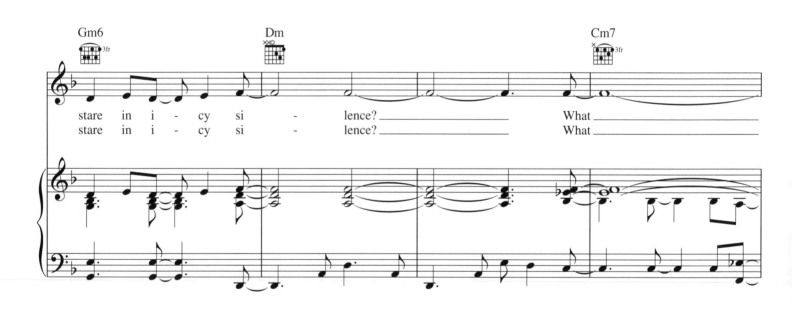

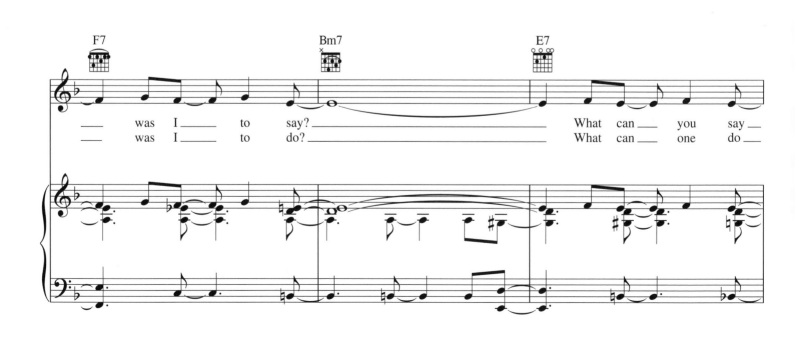

when a love af - fair is o - ver? ____

when a love ____

____ af - fair is o - ver? ____

rit.

Portuguese Lyrics

A insensatez
Que você fez
Coração mais sem cuidado
Fez chorar de dôr
O seu amôr
Um amôr tão delicado
Ah! Porque você
Foi fraco assim
Assim tão desalmado
Ah! Meu coração
Que nunca amou
Não merece ser amado
Vai meu coração
Ouve a razão
Usa só sinceridade
Quem semeia vento
Diz a razão
Colhe tempestade
Vai meu coração
Pede perdão
Perdão apaixonado
Vai porque
Quem não
Pede perdão
Não é nunca perdoado.

I CAN'T MAKE YOU LOVE ME

Words and Music by MIKE REID
and ALLEN SHAMBLIN

I GOTTA RIGHT TO SING THE BLUES

Words by TED KOEHLER
Music by HAROLD ARLEN

*Women may sing down one octave.

I GUESS I'LL HANG MY TEARS OUT TO DRY

Words by SAMMY CAHN
Music by JULE STYNE

I LEFT MY HEART IN SAN FRANCISCO

Words by DOUGLASS CROSS
Music by GEORGE CORY

I SHOULD CARE

Words and Music by SAMMY CAHN,
PAUL WESTON and AXEL STORDAHL

I WILL WAIT FOR YOU

from THE UMBRELLAS OF CHERBOURG

Music by MICHEL LEGRAND
Original French Text by JACQUES DEMY
English Words by NORMAN GIMBEL

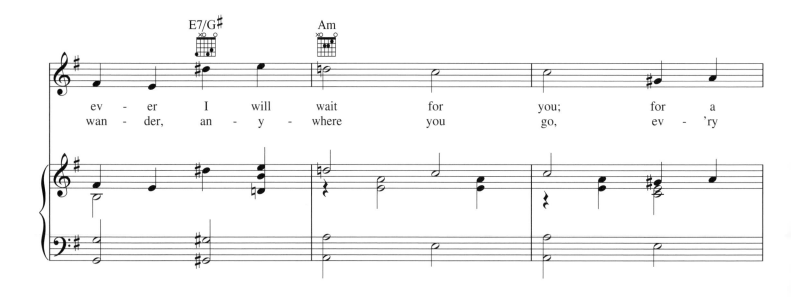

I WISH I DIDN'T LOVE YOU SO

from the Paramount Picture THE PERILS OF PAULINE

Words and Music by
FRANK LOESSER

140

I'LL NEVER SMILE AGAIN

Words and Music by
RUTH LOWE

I WISH YOU LOVE

English Words by ALBERT BEACH
French Words and Music by CHARLES TRENET

I'LL KNOW
from GUYS AND DOLLS

By FRANK LOESSER

I'LL NEVER LOVE THIS WAY AGAIN

Words and Music by RICHARD KERR
and WILL JENNINGS

I'M A FOOL TO WANT YOU

Words and Music by JACK WOLF,
JOEL HERRON and FRANK SINATRA

I'M STILL IN LOVE WITH YOU

Words and Music by AL GREEN,
WILLIE MITCHELL and AL JACKSON, JR.

162

I'VE NEVER BEEN IN LOVE BEFORE

from GUYS AND DOLLS

By FRANK LOESSER

IN THE BLUE OF EVENING

Words by TOM ADAIR
Music by D'ARTEGA

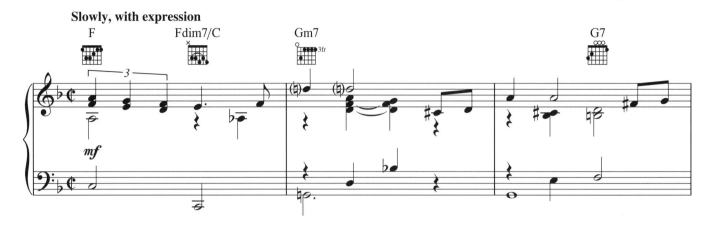

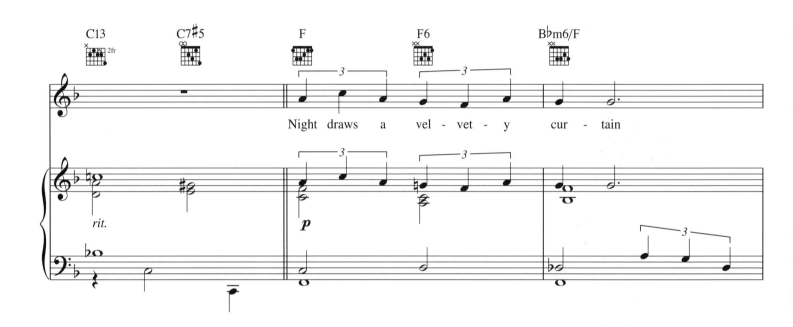

Night draws a vel-vet-y cur-tain

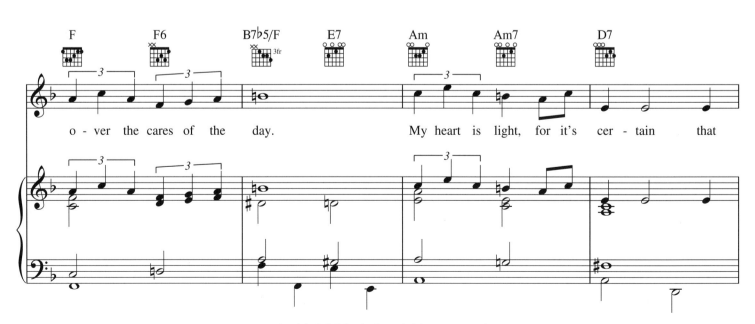

o-ver the cares of the day. My heart is light, for it's cer-tain that

I'll be meet-ing you in se-cret ren-dez-vous: In the blue of

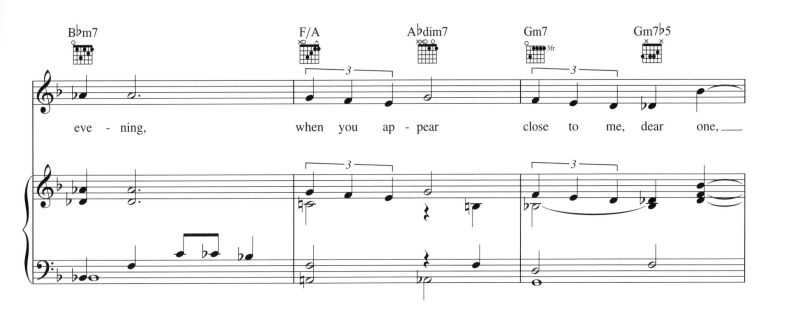

eve - ning, when you ap - pear close to me, dear one, ____

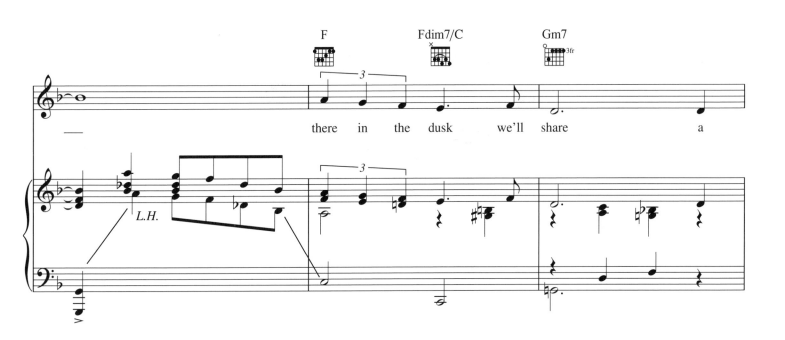

____ there in the dusk we'll share a

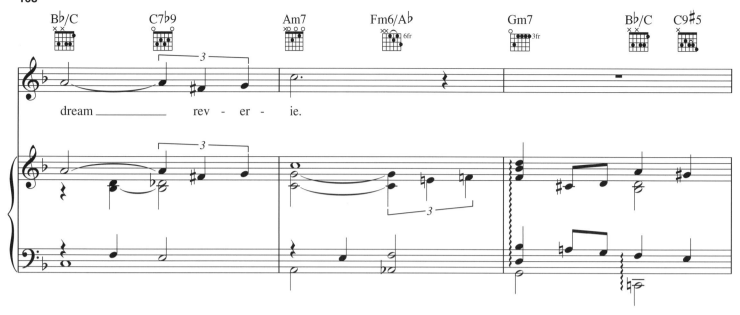

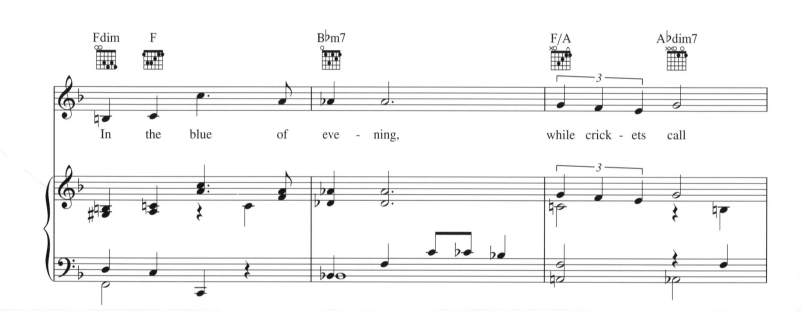

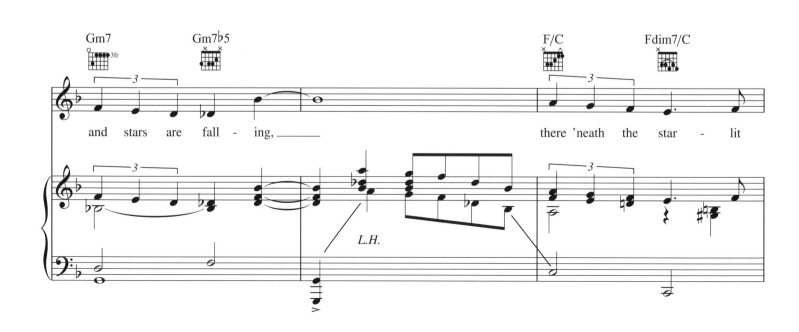

IS THAT ALL THERE IS

Words and Music by JERRY LEIBER
and MIKE STOLLER

Moderately

Spoken: I remember when I was a very little {girl/boy}... our house caught on

fire... I'll never forget the look on my father's face as he gathered me up in his arms and raced thru

the burning building out onto the pavement... I stood there shivering in my pajamas... and watched the whole world go

Let's break out the booze and have a ball, if that's all there is. Spoken: And when I was twelve years old my father took me to the circus... the greatest show on earth... there were clowns and elephants and dancing

IT ALL DEPENDS ON YOU

from THE SINGING FOOL

Words and Music by B.G. DeSYLVA, LEW BROWN
and RAY HENDERSON

JUST ONE MORE CHANCE

Words by SAM COSLOW
Music by ARTHUR JOHNSTON

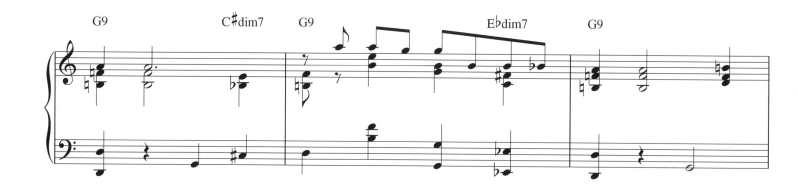

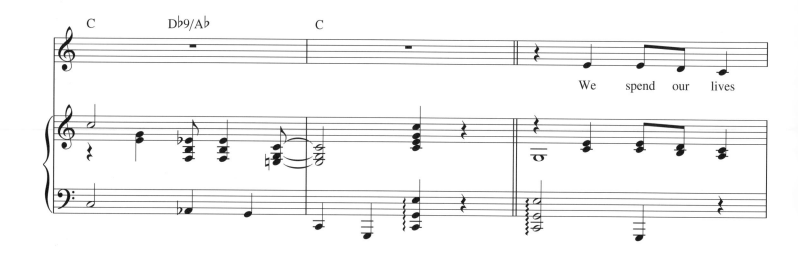

We spend our lives

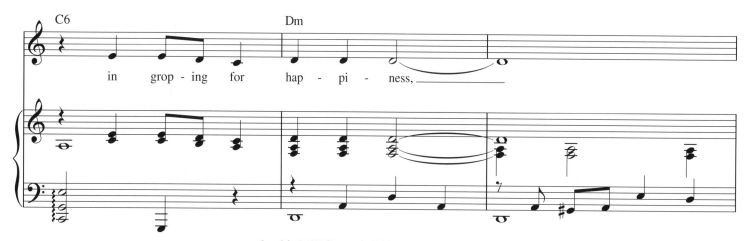

in grop-ing for hap-pi-ness,

184

LOVE, LOOK AWAY

from FLOWER DRUM SONG

Lyrics by OSCAR HAMMERSTEIN II
Music by RICHARD RODGERS

Lento

I have wished be - fore. I will wish no

Moderato espressivo
Refrain

more. Love, look a - way! _____ Love, look a - way from

me. Fly, when you pass my door, Fly and get lost at

LOVER, COME BACK TO ME

from THE NEW MOON

Lyrics by OSCAR HAMMERSTEIN II
Music by SIGMUND ROMBERG

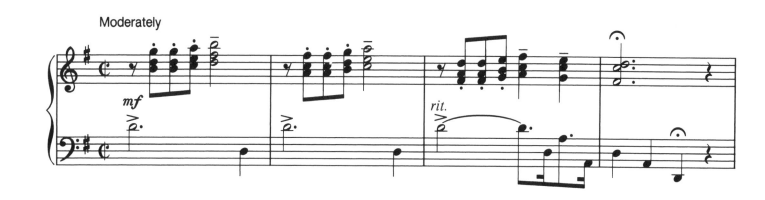

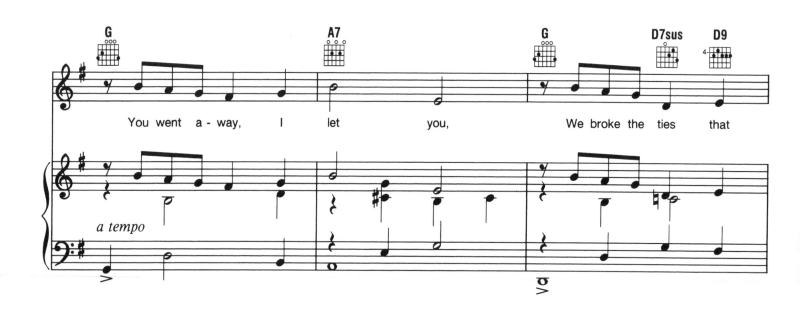

You went a-way, I let you, We broke the ties that

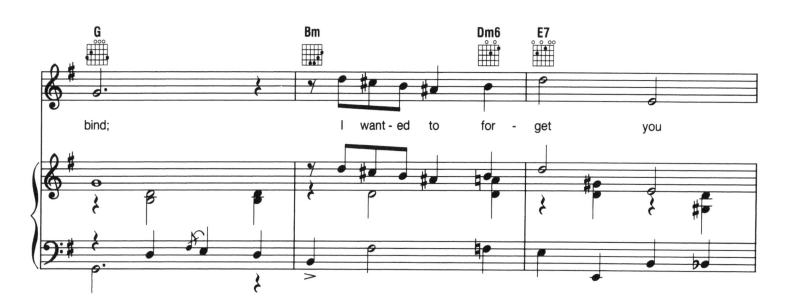

bind; I want-ed to for-get you

LUSH LIFE

Words and Music by
BILLY STRAYHORN

LOVER MAN
(Oh, Where Can You Be?)

By JIMMY DAVIS,
ROGER RAMIREZ and JIMMY SHERMAN

MAYBE THIS TIME

from the Musical CABARET

Words by FRED EBB
Music by JOHN KANDER

MEAN TO ME

Lyric and Music by FRED E. AHLERT
and ROY TURK

MORE THAN YOU KNOW

Words by WILLIAM ROSE and EDWARD ELISCU
Music by VINCENT YOUMANS

212

THE NEARNESS OF YOU

from the Paramount Picture ROMANCE IN THE DARK

Words by NED WASHINGTON
Music by HOAGY CARMICHAEL

MY OLD FLAME
from the Paramount Picture BELLE OF THE NINETIES

Words and Music by ARTHUR JOHNSTON
and SAM COSLOW

MY SILENT LOVE

Words by EDWARD HEYMAN
Music by DANA SUESSE

RAINY DAYS AND MONDAYS

Lyrics by PAUL WILLIAMS
Music by ROGER NICHOLS

SINCE I DON'T HAVE YOU

Words and Music by JAMES BEAUMONT,
JANET VOGEL, JOSEPH VERSCHAREN,
WALTER LESTER, LENNIE MARTIN,
JOSEPH ROCK and JOHN TAYLOR

Slowly, with a strong, rockin' beat

SOMEWHERE ALONG THE WAY

Words by SAMMY GALLOP
Music by KURT ADAMS

STORMY WEATHER
(Keeps Rainin' All the Time)
from COTTON CLUB PARADE OF 1933

Lyric by TED KOEHLER
Music by HAROLD ARLEN

Don't know why _____ there's no sun up in the sky, Storm - y Weath - er, _____

Since my man and I ain't to - geth - er, _____ keeps rain - in' all _ the time. _____

Life is bare, _____ gloom and mis - 'ry ev - 'ry - where, Storm - y Weath - er, _____

Interlude

TELL ME ON A SUNDAY
from SONG AND DANCE

Music by ANDREW LLOYD WEBBER
Lyrics by DON BLACK

Slowly (♩ = 63)

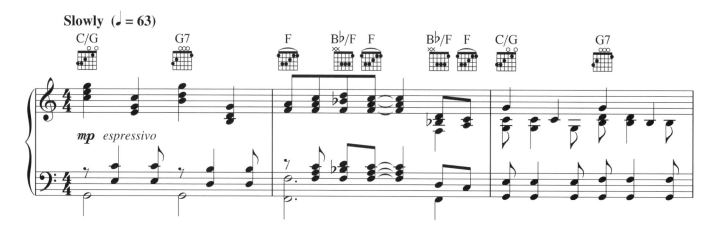

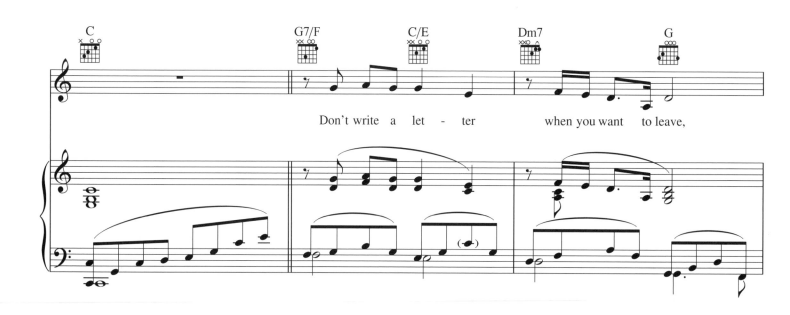

Don't write a let - ter when you want to leave,

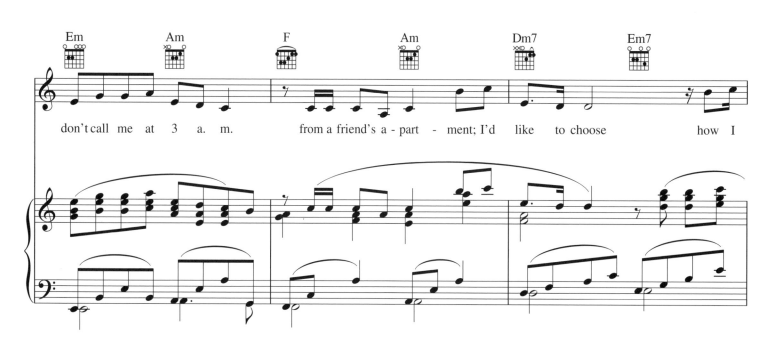

don't call me at 3 a. m. from a friend's a - part - ment; I'd like to choose how I

246

THE THRILL IS GONE

from GEORGE WHITE'S SCANDALS (1931 Edition)

Words by LEW BROWN
Music by RAY HENDERSON

THANKS FOR THE MEMORY

from the Paramount Picture BIG BROADCAST OF 1938

Words and Music by LEO ROBIN
and RALPH RAINGER

UNCHAINED MELODY
from the Motion Picture UNCHAINED

Lyric by HY ZARET
Music by ALEX NORTH

THE VERY THOUGHT OF YOU

Words and Music by
RAY NOBLE

UNTIL IT'S TIME FOR YOU TO GO
from ELVIS ON TOUR

Words and Music by
BUFFY SAINTE-MARIE

Moderately fast

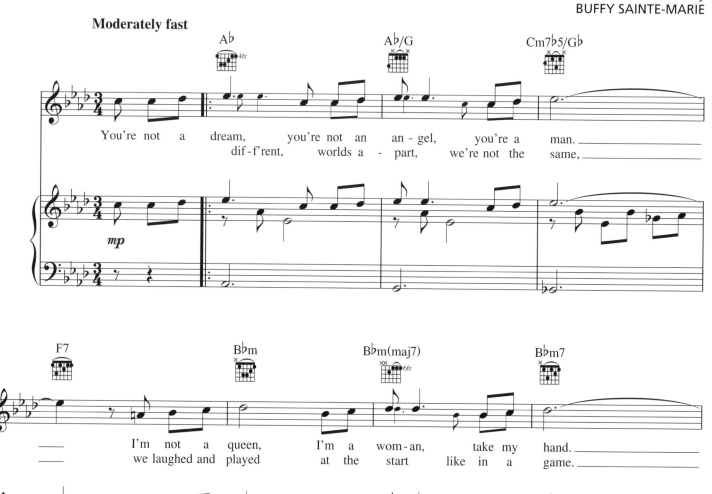

You're not a dream, you're not an an-gel, you're a man. ___
dif-f'rent, worlds a-part, we're not the same, ___

___ I'm not a queen, I'm a wom-an, take my hand. ___
___ we laughed and played at the start like in a game. ___

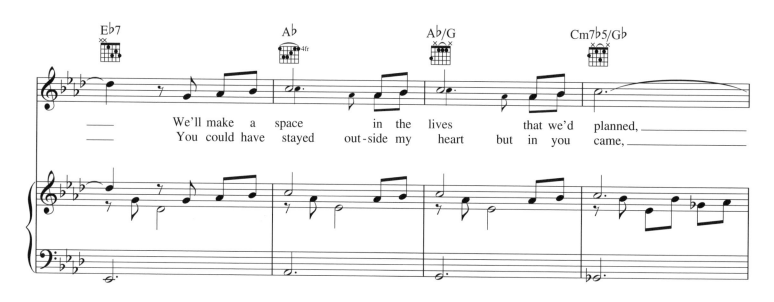

___ We'll make a space in the lives that we'd planned, ___
___ You could have stayed out-side my heart but in you came, ___

WHAT I DID FOR LOVE

from A CHORUS LINE

Music by MARVIN HAMLISCH
Lyric by EDWARD KLEBAN

Slowly

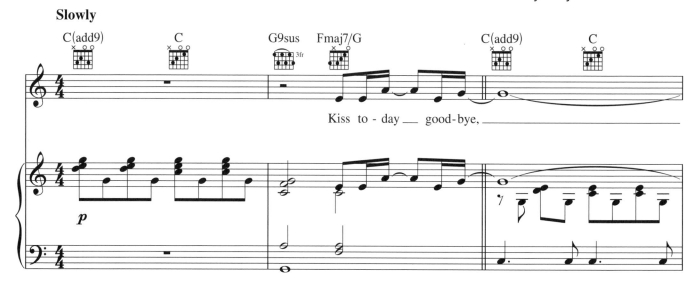

Kiss to-day ___ good-bye,

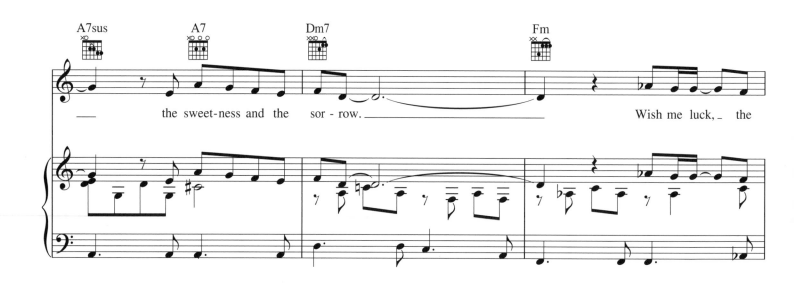

___ the sweet-ness and the sor-row. ___ Wish me luck, ___ the

same to you. ___ But I can't re-gret ___

WHAT KIND OF FOOL AM I?

from the Musical Production STOP THE WORLD–I WANT TO GET OFF

Words and Music by LESLIE BRICUSSE
and ANTHONY NEWLEY

Moderately slow

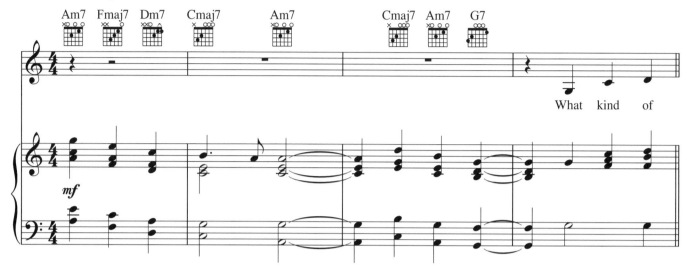

What kind of

fool am I? _____ Who nev-er fell in love, _____ it seems that

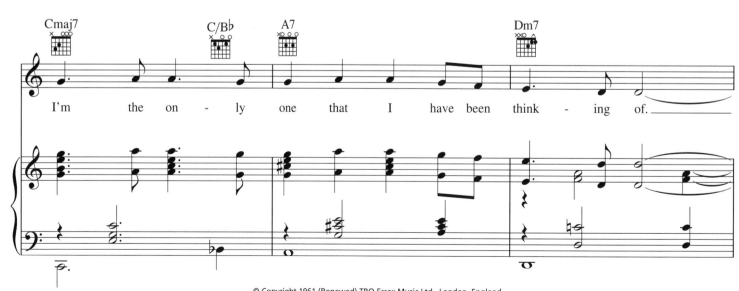

I'm the on-ly one that I have been think-ing of. _____

YOU DON'T BRING ME FLOWERS

Words by NEIL DIAMOND,
MARILYN BERGMAN and ALAN BERGMAN
Music by NEIL DIAMOND

WHEN SUNNY GETS BLUE

Lyric by JACK SEGAL
Music by MARVIN FISHER

Slow Blues tempo

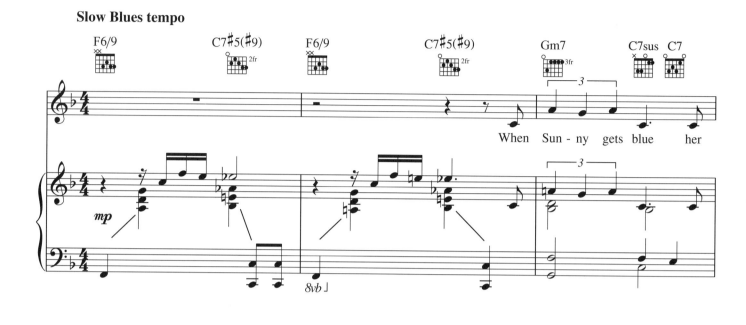

When Sun-ny gets blue her

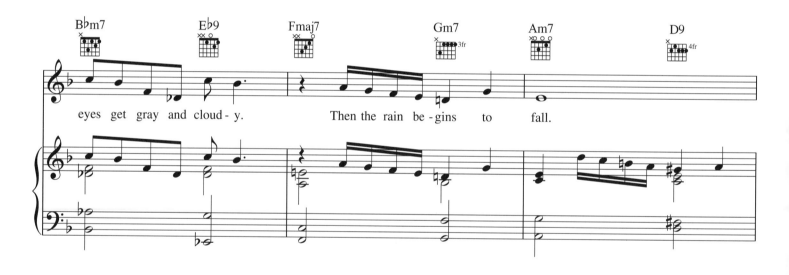

eyes get gray and cloud-y. Then the rain be-gins to fall.

Pit-ter pat-ter, pit-ter pat-ter, love is gone so what can mat-ter?

WHY WAS I BORN?

from SWEET ADELINE

Lyrics By OSCAR HAMMERSTEIN II
Music by JEROME KERN

YESTERDAY ONCE MORE

Words and Music by JOHN BETTIS
and RICHARD CARPENTER

Moderate Ballad

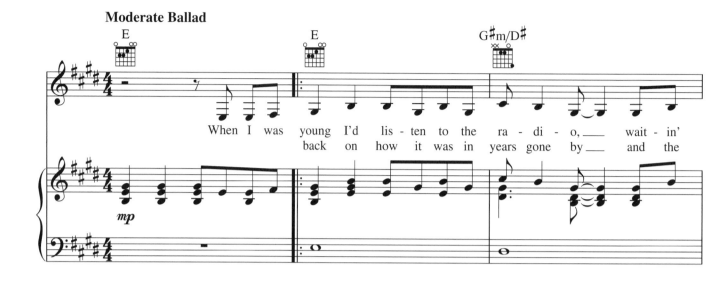

When I was young I'd lis-ten to the ra-di-o,___ wait-in'
back on how it was in years gone by ___ and the

for my fa-v'rite songs. ___ When they played, I'd sing a - long;
good times that I had, ___ makes to - day seem rath - er sad; ___

it made me smile. ___
so much has changed. ___

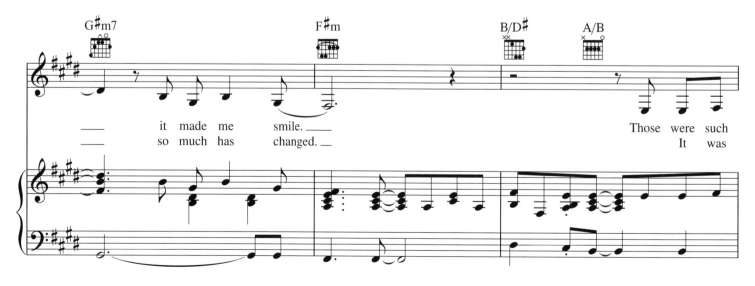

Those were such
It was

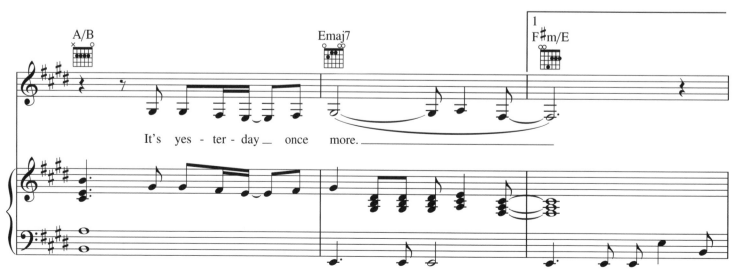

shing - a - ling - a - ling that they're start - ing to sing's _ so fine. _

When they get to the part _ where he's break - in' her heart, _ it can
All my best mem - o - ries _ come back clear - ly to me; _ some can

real - ly make me cry _ just like be - fore. _
e - ven make me cry _

It's yes - ter - day _ once more. _

YOU DON'T KNOW WHAT LOVE IS

Words and Music by DON RAYE
and GENE DePAUL